Red Squi~~r~~

by

Helen Butler

*Red Squirrels
on the Isle of Wight
&
How grey squirrels have outcompeted
red squirrels elsewhere*

Red Squirrels on the Isle of Wight
by
Helen Butler

This book is dedicated to all the
volunteers, sponsors, friends and family
without whose support, moral and financial,
running Wight Squirrel Project
would not be possible

Printed by Crossprint
Newport Business Park
21 Barry Way
Newport
Isle of Wight
PO30 5GY

Contents

PREFACE

This poem by local lady Mary Ralph, sums up our native red squirrel perfectly.

The Red Squirrel *(In an Isle of Wight wood)*
I walked in peaceful solitude
Through a woodland glade,
And on, beneath a canopy,
Of lovely dappled shade.
The honeysuckle's sweet perfume
Filled the evening air,
To proclaim a gift of nature
For each and all to share.

And though alone, yet not alone,
I glanced towards the skies.
And chanced to see a small red squirrel,
Bringing pleasure to my eyes,
But of me, it seemed quite unaware,
I dared not move or speak,
But teased it, oh! so playfully
In a game of hide and seek.

For in secrecy I stood to watch
It scamper through the trees,
With fluffy tail held up aloft
Like a sail to catch the breeze.
I marvelled at it's summer coat
A chestnut red so bright
And so too, at it's tufted ears,
Brush stroke tipped with creamy white.

Then came the evening twilight.
I left that tranquil scene,
Leaving only footprints,
To show that I had been.
And as I held that moment,
Thoughts inside me loomed,
If this were not an island,
My red squirrel, would well be doomed.

Mary Ralph

Introducing Squirrels

To the majority of people   living in the British Isles today, the mention of squirrels conjures up an image of the American grey squirrel. But for those privileged few who live in a 'red squirrel only' area, there is no more gratifying experience than watching our native species. The reds are elusive and timid by nature, adding to their appeal - and your thrill - at seeing this most charismatic of our native woodland mammals.

Squirrels belong to the order Rodentia, of which there are 1650 species worldwide.   Rodents are characterized by their grinding molars and   their   incisors,   which   grow   throughout   their   life. Rodents are split into 3 main groups depending on how their jaw muscles are attached to the cheekbone. It's a misconception that squirrels   belong to the same group as rats.   Both red and grey squirrels are one of 267 species of 'tree squirrels' worldwide, belonging to the group Sciuridae. The familiar chipmunks and flying squirrels are included in this group. Therefore both red and grey squirrels are actually tree squirrels and not tree rats.

> **SQUIRREL FACT**
> Latin name for red squirrels -Sciurus vulgaris. Latin name for American grey squirrels - Sciurus carolinensis.

Red squirrels are our native species and definitely win the prize for being fascinating, cute and enigmatic. People with 'garden' red squirrels often consider them part of the family. Those who have only ever had grey squirrels in the garden may view them with equal affection. For this reason, and the fact that the majority of the country are only familiar with greys, they are included in this book. Also, our native red squirrel's story is inextricably linked with that of the introduced American grey squirrel.

Sightings of our native red squirrel are frequent on the Isle of Wight. Island woods are relatively small and fragmented and often near roads or development, giving a greater chance of seeing a red squirrel. Red squirrels are not shy about helping themselves to peanuts put out for the birds, so there are literally hundreds of homes on the Island that have these delightful animals visiting daily.

'Garden squirrels' on the Isle of Wight

History

Historically our native red squirrels colonised the whole of the British Isles. Then, in 1867, a Mr Brocklehurst introduced grey squirrels into Henbury Park in Cheshire. This introduction was followed by 30 releases elsewhere in the country, thus sealing the red squirrel's fate in mainland Britain.

Woodland destruction throughout the British Isles will naturally reduce the number of squirrels. Over the years, tree loss due to development and modern farming methods has decreased woodland cover - and the vital hedges linking woods together. Small, isolated populations may be wiped out in bad seed crop years and not replaced if 'corridors' linking woods together are lost.

Disease has also played a major role in the decline of reds, as they appear to be more susceptible to certain diseases than greys. Although not the sole reason for the reds' decline, the greys were certainly a major contributory factor. If the greys had not been introduced into Britain, then it's highly probable red squirrel numbers would have recovered from times of natural disease, habitat fragmentation and years of food shortage.

The Isle of Wight is fortunate in having the Solent as a barrier to direct grey squirrel invasion. Although the odd grey squirrel has mysteriously found it's way to the Island in the past and has been quickly dealt with. However, the Isle of Wight squirrels have not been spared the landscape changes that also affect the rest of the country.

'Prairie' farming

From the Neolithic period onwards the needs of agriculture have altered the Island's landscape. When hedgerows and small fields were common, it's said that squirrels could travel from one end of the Island to the other. This is certainly no longer the case! In the south of the Island, lighter soils have provided good agricultural land and there are no sizeable woods left.

The heavier clay soils in the north are much harder to work and tree cover is higher. This is where the majority of our squirrels are found.

When I started working with red squirrels on the Island in 1991, numbers had dropped to a low level as a result of the 1987 hurricane. Apart from the tree loss and the inevitable decrease in winter food, corridors links were disrupted, leaving some woods isolated. People who had fed squirrels in their garden for years reported their loss. However, numbers rose steadily throughout the 1990's and once again red squirrels are seen regularly in gardens, parks and woods.

---

*Fossil remains of the red squirrel found in Britain were dated at between 7,000 and 10,000 years old.

*Red squirrels were widespread over the whole of the British Isles and Ireland after the last Ice Age.

*Red squirrels disappeared from Ireland in the 15th century and were not reintroduced until the 19th century. It's believed deforestation was responsible for their disappearance.

*In Wales and Scotland, squirrels rapidly declined during timber shortages in the 15th and 16th centuries. During the 18th century Scottish red squirrel numbers plummeted almost to the point of extinction. The reason is unknown.

*The beginning of the 19th century saw tree planting on a large scale, especially of fast growing conifers.

*Greys introduced into Cheshire.

*By 1900 red squirrel numbers were high Between 1900 and 1925 reds suffered a dramatic decline in the British Isles. Natural disease cycles exacerbated by overcrowding, food shortage, bad weather, habitat destruction and pressure from grey squirrels, all contributed to this decline.

*Timber requirements for the Second World War and a series of harsh winters hastened the decline in reds. Greys expanded, being better suited to exploit broadleaved woodland.

*Red numbers have declined rapidly during the last 60 years. This decline is mirrored by the rise in grey squirrels.

Table showing the history of red squirrel decline

Distribution of Red and Grey Squirrels

Worldwide
Red squirrels are found across a broad band of territory running from the seaboard of Western Europe and Scandinavia through the former USSR and Mongolia to North East China. Unfortunately, grey squirrels were introduced into Italy and again the reds have declined as the number of greys has risen - just as it has in Britain. Once over the Alps there will be little to stop grey squirrels eventually taking over the whole of the reds' range. Greys are abundant in their native country, North America.

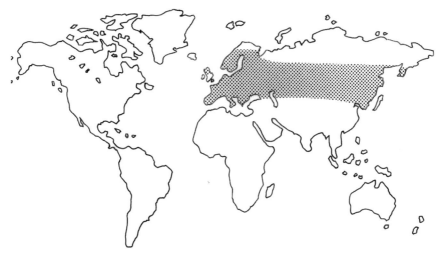

World distribution of red squirrels

Great Britain
In southern England, red squirrels are now only found on the islands in Poole Harbour and on the Isle of Wight. The Isle of Wight is seen as nationally important as it offers an opportunity to maintain a population of around 3000 reds in predominantly broadleaved habitat.

During the winter of 2002/2003 I visited 277 woods over 1hectare (2.4 acres) on the Island and of these, 238 had resident squirrels. The smaller woods, under 1ha. also have squirrels, so most of the woods have resident squirrels. Isolation and unsuitable tree species are the main reasons for woodland without squirrels.

In the north of England, the Lake district and Scotland, greys are still pursuing their relentless march into red squirrel territory. At present, reds are still living in the pure conifer plantations in Scotland.

In Wales there are a few scattered populations and Northern Ireland still has pockets of red squirrels. Greys are present in large numbers in both countries. There is also a small population of reds - living without an immediate grey squirrel threat - in Jersey.

Corsican pine plantation, excellent habitat for red squirrels

The Competition Between Reds and Greys

Greys have not taken over simply because they are the larger and more aggressive species, they outcompete, rather than directly kill the smaller reds. Greys evolved in broadleaved woodland in North America and can use this type of woodland more effectively than reds, as they can digest the tannins in acorns, which the reds cannot. Also, greys will strip the hazel crop early in the season and then move onto the acorns leaving the reds living in deciduous woodland short of food. Greys gain weight on a diet of acorns but reds lose weight and may contract gastroenteritis.

A grey squirrel eating an acorn

Greys live in denser numbers, (more per hectare) and as they have more kittens (baby squirrels) per litter, their numbers grow faster. In overcrowded conditions reds stop breeding and may die of stress.

Researchers have also noticed that greys chase red females during the mating season which is thought to inhibit red breeding success. Although cousins, red and grey squirrels are too genetically different to interbreed.

A devastating disease that the greys carry, but rarely contract, is parapoxvirus. Reds contract and die of this virus which spreads through the population very quickly. The time between seeing the first grey in a red only area and the complete disappearance of the reds is approximately 15 years.

SQUIRREL FACT
Reds put on 10% bodyweight before the winter - greys 20% thus giving them a competitive edge in a bad winter.

Red and Grey Identification

It can be difficult to distinguish between red and grey squirrels. Colour alone is certainly not reliable. A red squirrel's coat colour varies enormously – from silvery grey to black and all shades of brown and ginger. The grey coloured reds are often confused with grey squirrels so you need to look carefully for the differences.

Greys never have eartufts. Their coat is a mottled grey, which hardly varies between animals - except when they are moulting when their coat can look red. The tail has 3 colours in it – black, red and white. If you think you have seen a grey squirrel, look at the tail, it has a distinct white halo which a red squirrel's tail never does. Greys are almost twice the size of reds and of chunkier build. Behaviour is another clue. Greys are much bolder, spend more time on the ground and are less likely to run away from you.

The distinctive tail of a grey squirrel.

Note the three coloured banding and the white 'halo'.

A red squirrel never has this 'halo'.

Size and weight comparison between red and grey squirrels		
	Red	Grey
Body length	220mm	260mm
Tail length	180mm	220mm
Weight	300g	550g

Spot the difference between red and grey squirrels

A red squirrel with a grey coloured coat.

Notice the coat is a uniform grey and not 'mottled'.

The tail does not have the distinctive banding.

This photograph was taken in the winter, so the red squirrel has eartufts.

This red squirrel has a very dark grey winter coat and very large eartufts.

This colouring still does cause confusion and is sometimes misidentified as a grey squirrel.

A grey squirrel. It has pointed ears but no tufts.

The coat is distinctly 'mottled' rather than a uniform colour.

Both species have white bellies.

Feeding

The mainstay of the diet for both species of squirrel is seeds, berries and nuts.   Deciduous woods can offer a wider variety of food if there is a good mix of tree species.   Grey squirrels do well in this type of woodland. Pure conifer plantations can provide cones all the year round, especially if they have plenty of Scots pine, as the cones are ready earlier in the season than the other conifers.   Red squirrels can reach high numbers in conifer plantations and are able to compete with the greys, who do not fare well solely on the small seeds of pine cones.

Autumn
Autumn should bring a bonanza of food in the form of nuts, seeds, fruit and fungi. This is the time when squirrels - red and grey -bury excess food.

Sweet chestnut Hazel Beech Acorns Field maple keys
Alder seeds Berries
Pine and various other conifer seeds
Fungi - Vuilleminia, that grows on oak, is a favourite

Winter
During the winter months squirrels eat the food they cached in the autumn. Caches may be buried in the ground or in the niche of a tree.   There are different lines of thought as to how squirrels know how to retrieve these hidden hoards. Do they keep a map in their head or do they rely on their keen sense of smell?

Pine and various other conifer seeds
Bark Fungi Bulbs Buds Leaves

SQUIRREL FACT
Teeth grow throughout a squirrel's life and are worn down by constant gnawing.

SQUIRREL FACT
A red squirrel living in a pine plantation will eat around 40,000 cones a year. This is about 2 million seeds.

Spring
As spring and early summer arrives, food becomes scarcer. Flowers, shoots and buds are a poor substitute for nuts and berries. Wych elm and wild cherry can provide a valuable food source but they are relatively scarce in our woodlands.
Reds can eat oak leaves early in the season but leaves become tougher and contain more tannins, to deter insects, after June. Spring and early summer is a time when the death toll starts to rise.

Pine and various other pine seeds   Bark   Buds
Shoots Leaves Catkins   Pollen
Insects Birds eggs Carrion
Ripening ears of grain
Squirrels will scavenge in dustbins if they are very hungry

Summer
For red squirrels living in forests with Scots pine, the summer food shortage is not so acute as cones are ready to eat early on in the summer, usually around June. Although still green, the squirrels munch their way through the cones, eating virtually everything as the spines are not yet hard. As the cones mature, only the seeds are taken and the rest discarded. Corsican pine cones will mature later in the summer. Greys eat hazelnuts early, before they are ripe.

Bark Ash keys Field maple keys Crab apple
Blackberries   Rose hip
Leaves and shoots
Insects

SQUIRREL FACT
Squirrels know if a nut is no good by the weight and will not waste time opening it. The average time for splitting open and eating a hazel nut is 22 seconds.

Breeding

Squirrels will not mate unless there is a good food supply and they are fit. Mating chases start early in the year. The males are attracted by the females scent as she comes into season. She is only ready to mate for 1 day, twice a year, and will scent mark trees as a signal she is coming into season. Tail swishing and loud chattering calls are followed by chasing through the trees. Several males chase a single red female, but over 30 males have been recorded chasing a single female grey squirrel and competitors can become violent.

The first brood of young, called kittens, are usually born between March and April after 38-42 days gestation. Females rear their young alone. An average litter of reds is 2 or 3. Greys may have 5 or 6 kittens per litter.

After 12 weeks with their mother, the kittens have to find their own home range and fend for themselves. If there is still a good food supply, a second brood will be born in the summer. Year old females only produce one litter in their first breeding season.

A full term red squirrel foetus.

The mother had fallen into a trough full of water and died of exhaustion trying to get out.

She had given birth, in the water, to this kitten's sibling.

At birth, kittens weigh 10g-15g and measure about 6-7cm from the top of the head to the base of the tail.

A question I am often asked refers to telling the difference between male and female squirrels. The best way is to wait until they hang upside down, facing you, on a peanut feeder and look for the obvious! There is no difference in size or colour between males and females!

A male squirrel.

In the breeding season, which is between January and September,it is easy to tell if a squirrel is an adult male.

The testes are large and cannot be missed!

An immature male will be harder to identify.

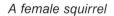
A female squirrel

A female squirrel that is feeding babies is easily identified by the 4 pairs of nipples

A mating chase

A very young red squirrel, just after weaning

* Kittens are born blind, toothless and hairless.
* By about 2 weeks old they will be covered with hair.
* After four weeks the eyes and ears are open and the teeth will start to appear.
* Although still suckling, the youngsters leave the nest and try solid food at about 7 weeks.
* Lactation lasts about 10 weeks.   Females have 4 pairs of nipples.
* Between 10 and 14 weeks they will move away from the nest and live independently.
* At 12 weeks they may weigh 160g-220g and have a full set of milk teeth.
* At around 4 months the baby coat is moulted.
* Milk teeth are lost between 4 and 8 months of age.

Table showing the development of kittens

SQUIRREL FACT
Females move babies between nests by carrying them in their mouth, around their neck or on their back.

Squirrel Behaviour

In common with other species, most squirrel behaviour is based on the instinct to survive and breed. Dominant animals win the best territory and the fittest males mate with the females. Weak, young or subordinate animals are driven away from the wood or relegated to the poorest habitat. Chasing and aggressive postures are usually sufficient to sort out the pecking order but fights do occur.

Wounds heal very quickly and squirrels can adapt to the loss of a limb, although a disadvantaged squirrel will be lower in the pecking order. Gender alone does not determine dominance. Size and having an assertive nature are more likely to win the day whether they are male or female!

Whilst looking for their own home range, squirrels are more likely to travel further afield and find themselves in human habitat I have had reports of red squirrels in the town centre or entering shops and offices! Adult squirrels, particularly males, travel further in search of mates. Mating, food shortage, habitat disturbance and dispersal of young squirrels in the spring and autumn will account for most movement. It is during September and October that I have the most number of squirrels for post mortem, the majority having been killed crossing roads.

Grooming is a hasty affair. A quick lick and scratch is enough to maintain their beautiful coats. The tail is groomed last

Contrary to popular belief, neither species will hibernate during the winter months and will feed daily unless the weather is very bad, when they will stay in their drey. Both species are diurnal which means they are active during daylight hours only. Activity peaks at dawn, when they look for breakfast, and again at dusk. There may be another peak in late afternoon during the summer. Squirrels may rest slumped on a branch between times.

Resting in a tree.

Squirrels do not live in family groups, except for mother and babies in the first 3 months of life. If it's a matter of survival though, squirrels may huddle together in one drey - as a squirrels's nest is called - to keep warm.

Trees are where squirrels feel at home and reds especially so, as they spend far more time in the trees than greys and it's here they feel safe from most predators The tail waving and chattering you may have observed is a sign of annoyance or alarm when it sees you. Leaping into the nearest tree, freezing movement and flattening against the tree are natural reactions to being disturbed.

Leaping into the nearest tree when disturbed

Squirrels do have their own home ranges, which they defend, but they do roam outside these ranges and territories do overlap. If there is a good crop of nuts or cones in an area of woodland, squirrels will share the crop regardless of whose home range it is.

Squirrel Biology

Red and grey squirrels have evolved to cope with life in the trees. Vision, hearing, sense of smell and balance are acute. It is thought from the structure of the eye that squirrels are red green colour blind.

'Reversible' feet enables squirrels to run down trees as easily as they run up them

Reds spend far more time in the trees than greys and prefer to feed from a vantage point such as a tree stump

Close up of the pads on the bottom of a red squirrel's feet

They have powerful hind legs and feet with a double joint which can turn 180%, enabling them to run up or down tree trunks with equal dexterity. Sharp claws and pads on the bottom of their feet provide effective gripping tools. The tail, apart from being used as a signal, acts as a balance, helping them to move through the tree tops at lightening speed.

A red squirrel's build and light weight enables it to climb out to the very tips of the trees to take cones and nuts. The grey   squirrel is almost twice the weight and does not have this advantage.

Predators may catch an unwary squirrel on the ground but in the trees they are relatively safe from most threats.

Coat colour can vary enormously in red squirrels. but the classic ginger colouring with a bleached tail in the summer is thought to be typical of British red squirrels.

The dark coat colouring found in some UK squirrels,   possibly came from crossbreeding with continental reds introduced into the   UK in the 18th and 19th centuries.

A red squirrel with a'bleached' tail

In red squirrels, the summer coat is generally a different colour to the winter coat.

The winter coat is   moulted in the spring, face first and working backward.   The autumn moult starts at the rump and works forwards.

SQUIRREL FACT
Squirrels have 20 pairs of chromosomes - humans have 23 pairs.

Life and Death

It's strictly survival of the fittest! An average of 75% - 85% of young do not survive their first winter. The first brood of young have a slimmer chance of survival as they leave the nest when food is scarcest. For those who do survive until their first birthday, life expectancy in the wild can be around 6 years for reds and 9 years for greys - if they are lucky. Lack of nutritious food is the most common cause of death within the first year. This may be coupled with a hard winter or disease.

Sick red squirrel . This is a typical pose - on the ground, head down and tail over the back.

It is a natural process for numbers in a wood to fluctuate wildly according to the season, immigration, emigration, habitat disturbance and success or failure of the seed crop. Also, during the summer and autumn months, the number of kittens born inflate numbers, but road casualties, predators and natural deaths reduce numbers.

Where greys interact with reds, there is the added danger of spreading the Parapoxvirus. It's rare for a grey to contract the virus although they carry it. The symptoms resemble myxomatosis in that lesions and swellings appear on the face, especially around the eyes. There is also ulceration and scabs on the body and movement is difficult.

Squirrels also carry external parasites such as fleas, lice and mites which will can cause anaemia, followed by death, if the build up becomes too great. Internal parasites include worms and coccidiosis.

Red squirrels are prone to suffer from cold and wet conditions and will quickly die of exposure. Stress triggers weight loss and disease which will weaken the squirrel and may lead to its death. A variety of bacterial and virul diseases can attack squirrels and they are able to contract health problems that are similar to those experienced by humans, eg. gastroenteritis or perforated stomach ulcer.

Natural predators also take their toll of young or unwary squirrels. Foxes, magpies, crows, barn owls, birds of prey and pine martens(Scotland) have all been witnessed taking red squirrels. On the Island, I have seen instances of a magpie stabbing a red squirrel through the chest and of a crow breaking a squirrel's neck - both in gardens.

Natural predators

SQUIRREL FACT
Too many oily nuts such as peanuts, and particularly brazil nuts, can cause osteoporosis by retarding the absorption of calcium. Feed carrot and provide bone for squirrels to chew on.

Squirrels and Humans

When humans come into contact with wildlife and upset the natural balance there will be conflict and controversy. Where we have built our homes and roads through former squirrel habitat a number of problems arise. The obvious ones are traffic and pets. On the positive side, supplementary food provided by homeowners is helpful in times of shortage but squirrels must be kept off the ground away from pets. Ropes or branches will 'bridge the gaps' and keep squirrels off the ground - do try it - you will be rewarded with hours of entertainment.

A good example of how to keep red squirrels off the ground and feed safely

Most people love having squirrels in their garden, particularly the reds who are far less damaging than the greys. I know the Isle of Wight reds provide endless hours of entertainment and are commonly known as 'timewasters' as it becomes addictive to watch them. People who encourage greys into their garden doubtless view them with the same affection - although they can take up residence in lofts and cause damage to wiring!

> **SQUIRREL FACT**
> Red squirrels have been voted Britain's favourite wild animal.

Water butts and steep sided ponds are another danger. Squirrels are naturally curious and can squeeze into very small gaps. They are good swimmers but die of exhaustion trying to climb out of the butt. Rat traps and netting are other hazards. I have seen 2 squirrels on the Island that have been caught in Fenn traps. Both had pulled themselves free but had lost 3 legs in the process. They did not die of these horrific injuries and were actually healing without any sign of infection.

Fenn trap

Where gardens back onto woodland, cats may venture into the woods and catch squirrels. It is possible to buy a sonic cat collar, but a collar with several bells should be the least precaution taken where cats are likely to impact on any wildlife. If dogs are allowed to run unleashed in the wood they sometimes catch unwary -usually young - squirrels.

A cat with 'garden squirrels'. Most do not sit and watch!

SQUIRREL FACT
Squirrels are often used as logos and in advertising

There are ways of spoiling your garden squirrels. Squirrels will readily take up residence in artificial dreys if placed correctly and these provide a deluxe residence that is more secure than a nest woven from twigs and moss.

Squirrels will quickly work out how to use a 'squirrel only' feeder. These are provided to encourage reds. Feeders to keep squirrels from bird food are sold in many pet stores.It's common to feed squirrels on peanuts in wire feeders. However, too many peanuts can cause thinning of the bone and a mixed diet is best.

Artificial drey

Coconut, sunflower seed, apple, carrot and hazelnuts will help prevent this problem. Brazil nuts must never be fed as they can kill a squirrel.

Food must always be of good quality, as chemically treated or stale food can – and does – cause digestive problems and even death. It is vital that feeders are kept clean and food fresh to prevent the build up of bacteria and disease. Squirrels naturally lick water from leaves and drink from puddles and ponds, but they are glad of a drink of water during the drier months. Containers should be placed off the ground, near an escape route and water must be changed daily and kept clean.

Provide squirrels with a drink but keep them off the ground

Enjoying an apple

Using a squirrel only feeder. To help prevent the spread of disease, do not put more into the feeder than the squirrels will eat in one day.

Scrub feeders thoroughly once a week .

Try to vary the nuts and fruit given to maintain a balanced diet.

With patience, red squirrels can become accustomed to your presence - especially when they are hungry!

If a hedge or tree is cut, leaving a gap in a red squirrel's 'corridor' to a garden, then red squirrels may no longer visit. Greys are less fussy about travelling along the ground. If you are privileged enough to have red squirrels visiting your garden, then do look after them - they will give endless hours of pleasure and you will be helping an endangered species.

How to make a squirrel feeder

A guide to making squirrel only feeders.   Not to scale.
All measurements are approximate according to available wood.

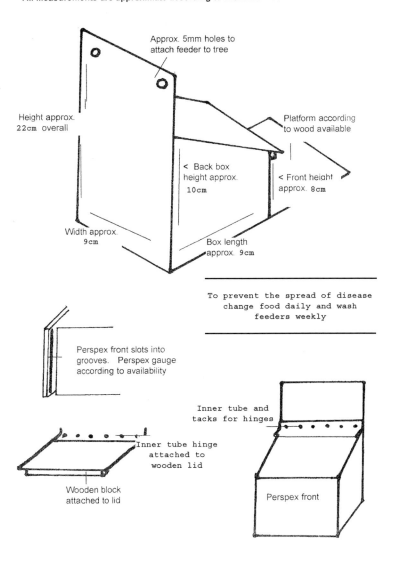

Approx. 5mm holes to
attach feeder to tree

Height approx.
22cm overall

Platform according
to wood available

< Back box
height approx.
10cm

< Front height
approx. 8cm

Width approx.
9cm

Box length
approx. 9cm

To prevent the spread of disease
change food daily and wash
feeders weekly

Perspex front slots into
grooves.   Perspex gauge
according to availability

Inner tube and
tacks for hinges

Inner tube hinge
attached to
wooden lid

Wooden block
attached to lid

Perspex front

How to make a squirrel drey

Sawn timber or
weatherproof ply
is recommended

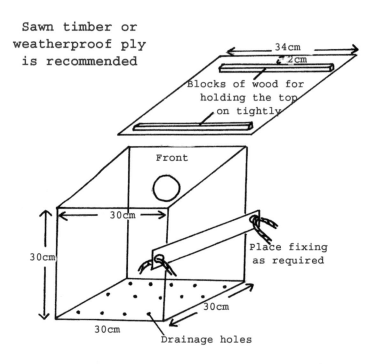

34cm

2cm

Blocks of wood for
holding the top
on tightly

Front

30cm

30cm

Place fixing
as required

30cm

30cm

30cm

Drainage holes

To affix drey to tree, attach
hooks or a bar as required.
Fix firmly to tree at least
8m above ground and facing
away from prevailing wind.
Fill with soft clean hay.

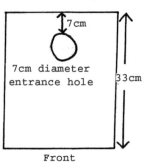

7cm

7cm diameter
entrance hole

33cm

Front

Where squirrels live

Woodlands, parks and gardens are where squirrels of both species are found, as their natural food is mainly seeds, nuts and fruit. The quality of habitat determines how many squirrels a wood 'carries', ie. how many squirrels it can sustain. Tree species, age and woodland management are the principal factors that determine habitat quality.

Grey squirrels thrive almost anywhere there are trees, although they do not fare as well in pure conifer plantations as our native reds. Greys evolved in the mixed deciduous woods of North America and do particularly well in British native oak woodlands. They also feed and scavenge in parks and gardens. Reds will also feed in gardens and parks but live at

Feeding a grey squirrel in the park

Dormouse

lower numbers per hectare than greys. Squirrels share the woods - and food supply - with other species. Birds and other small mammals compete for nuts and seeds. Nest sites, particularly tree hollows are sought after by birds such as owls and woodpeckers as well as squirrels. If there are large numbers of grey squirrels in a deciduous wood, then they can have quite an impact on birds and other small mammals.

SQUIRREL FACT

Greys in particular strip bark and kill young plantation trees. This may be to obtain food or as aggressive behaviour. The most serious damage occurs between May and July when food is short and breeding activity high.

A squirrel's nest is called a drey. Dreys are approximately 30cm in diameter and have no obvious entrance. They are usually built in mature trees at least 8m from the ground and generally against the trunk. Not every squirrel conforms to these building standards. I have seen dreys perched precariously on the end of branches or balanced on an outstretched hazel stem.

The outside is made of twigs which will initially have leaves on. The inside is lined with dried grass, leaves or moss to make soft, warm, dry home. Summer dreys are little more than a platform of twigs and leaves and are not built to last. Winter dreys are very well made and can last for several years. There is no obvious difference between red and grey squirrel dreys.

A tree hollow is the ultimate home and called a den. Squirrels build more than one drey so they may move home when the build up of fleas becomes unbearable.

A red squirrel entering it's den

The woven lining inside a drey

Red squirrels spend considerably more time in the trees than grey squirrels. Reds living in coniferous woodland are able to forage in the tree tops for most of the year. Shoots, catkins, fungi, green cones and ripe cone seeds are available to them in this lofty dining table.

Broadleaved woodland is another matter. Autumn fruits and seeds provide the mainstay of the year's food supply and has to be cached. This food supply has to be buried - or sometimes pushed into tree crevices - but usually buried in the ground. This means time spent on the ground burying food and again looking for caches and digging them up again. Caches are located by smell and the squirrel that retrieves this buried treasure is not necessarily the squirrel that buried it.

Seeds that are not retrieved may germinate, so the squirrels are unwittingly dispersing seed for the trees they rely on for food.

A squirrel drey high up in the fork of a tree

Retrieving buried food

Conservation and Conflicts

The introduced American grey squirrel is considered vermin and so there are no laws to protect it and no conservation efforts to help it - not that it needs any! The red squirrel on the other hand is a priority species for conservation action.   There is a national strategy to conserve reds, as well as local strategies in areas where they are still present.

The islands in Poole Harbour, the Isle of Wight and Jersey do not have greys at present and are seen as important areas for red squirrel conservation. These island populations have a better chance of survival in the long term and are considered nationally important.

Every effort is being made to save the remaining red squirrels in the north of England but it has proved extremely   difficult to prevent the greys' relentless march and once they have moved in, it is impossible to eradicate them.   Breeding and re-introduction programmes for red squirrels have been tried and tested for many years.   Unfortunately, due to the sensitive nature of the reds, these have proved problematical and largely unsuccessful.   It is a waste of time, money - and squirrels - to re-introduce reds where there are greys.

Greys are strong swimmers and could manage the distance to the islands in Poole Harbour and possibly the Isle of Wight if the currents were not so strong.   A grey squirrel does find its way across the Solent to the Isle of Wight occasionally, but public awareness and a strong commitment to keep the Island a 'red only' zone has, so far, succeeded. If a bridge or tunnel to the Isle of Wight should be built, then it's likely the island reds would be lost.

Red squirrels are able to co-exist with greys in pure pine plantations and can reach higher number per hectare. They are particularly fond of Scots and Corsican pine. Scots pine matures early in the summer when other food is short, providing the squirrels with a supply of green cones before other seeds mature. Conifers have a limited lifespan and must be felled and replanted approximately every 70 years. They will also need thinning so that the branches may spread out and produce better timber and more cones for the squirrels. It is best if the trees have a wide age range in plantations to ensure there is always some food for the squirrels. A conifer can take 35 years to start producing a good cone crop.

Woods are more productive both for commercial use and wildlife if they are managed. But as with most scenarios there is a conflict. Forestry work is commercially driven and the market price of timber, economies of scale and profit are normally the priority rather than conservation. Also it is more commercially viable to clear or thin large tracts of plantation rather than small areas at a time, which is disastrous for the squirrels if there is insufficient good habitat to move into.

For red squirrels living without a direct threat of grey squirrel invasion, a good mixture of tree species with about 24 standard trees per hectare plus an understorey of predominantly hazel is ideal. If the hazel is coppiced on a 15 year plus cycle, then so much the better. The problem is that this costs money as the hazel should be cut every 5-7 years for commercial use. This is too short a cycle for squirrels and other species such as dormice.

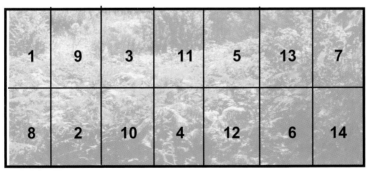

Adopt a 'chequerboard' plan for coppicing to prevent large unproductive areas in the wood

It's also important to ensure that no more than 25% of a wood is out of nut production and that there are no large unproductive areas. By using a 'chequerboard' plan for coppicing, it will help red squirrels and dormice to survive.

A wood with a wide variety of tree species is best, as seed crops for each species will fail periodically - but rarely in the same year. Hazel is an important food source for both red and grey squirrels but to provide a good supply of hazelnuts, mature hazel coppice with plenty of light is necessary.Hazel starts fruiting, given the right conditions, about 5 years after coppicing but it must have plenty of light to produce a good crop of nuts. Deer must be kept out of young coppice as they nibble the young shoots and retard growth. There are no deer on the Isle of Wight so hazel coppice regrowth is good.

Newly coppiced hazel

Regrowth after 1 year on the Isle of Wight where deer are absent

Survey Methods

There are a number of ways to check if there are squirrels in a woodland and whether they are grey or red. It is important to monitor squirrels - especially on the mainland where grey squirrels are encroaching into red squirrel areas.

Research that involves capturing, using radio collars, marking and taking samples from red squirrels, although useful and initially necessary, is often repeated. This method of monitoring can be harmful and stressful to reds who may die if handled. Technology could provide the answers to intensive and intrusive monitoring, rather than crude trapping methods.

A red squirrel having a radio collar fitted

A trapped red squirrel

By using the following methods an overall picture can be built up of squirrels in an area. Natural food supplies vary over the years as seed crops can either fail or provide a bumper supply of winter food. Such fluctuations impact heavily on the animals dependent upon them.   The population can halve or double accordingly, as the number of young surviving is largely dictated by food supply. In a poor year, weak or subordinate animals will also perish.

Where squirrels are fed in gardens adjacent to woodland, it is very noticeable that in years of good seed crop, they stay away for a 3 or 4 months. In years of poor seed crop, their absence to cache natural food in the wood is hardly noticed.

Hairtube Surveys

The concept of hairtube monitoring is very simple. The aim is to attract squirrels into baited tubes that have sticky pads either end. As the squirrel enters the tube to reach the food it rubs against the sticky pads, leaving hairs behind. These hairs are examined under a microscope to identify which species of squirrel they came from.

The tubes are plastic drainpipe cut into 30cm lengths with holes drilled either end to fix the wires that hold the tubes to the tree. The plastic blocks are approximately 2cm x 2cm and 7mm deep. Double-sided sticky tape is then wrapped around the block which is then stuck to the roof of the tube, at either end, about 2cm in.

Hairtube monitoring is used to establish whether there are squirrels in a wood and if they are red or grey. Under the microscope, you can see the difference between red and grey squirrel hairs - with a little practice!

A baited hairtube in a copse on the Isle of Wight

Drey counts

Dreys are semi-permanent and may be systematically counted. Squirrels are known to build more than one drey each, so an estimate of how many squirrels are living in the wood is calculated based on research for squirrels in either coniferous, mixed or deciduous woodland.

Feeding transects

Feeding transects are 50m x 1m of cleared ground beneath conifers. Uneaten cones and eaten cone cores are regularly (minimum once a year) collected and counted. From the used cones, an estimate of food eaten and the energy obtained is worked out. These figures are then converted to give squirrel density numbers.

Questionnaires

On the Island, I send out annual questionnaires to people who have 'garden' squirrels. They are asked if squirrel numbers have increased, decreased or are stable over the previous year. Seasonal numbers and the number of adults and babies are also recorded. These records give an indication of fluctuations in squirrel numbers in the area.

Sightings

Sightings from the general public, although not scientific, do provide a wealth of anecdotal data. This may be used to identify where further monitoring is required or perhaps where there is a 'squirrel road death' blackspot and signs or a crossing point needed.

Post mortems

Corpses can provide useful information on the state of health of squirrels. Although the majority of bodies recovered are killed by traffic or pets, post mortem examinations reveal breeding condition, general health and sometimes disease.

Woodland Walks

This method involves visual counts by walking a set transect 3 times within 2 weeks in the spring and autumn. One hundred metres is walked in 5 minutes, then the observer stops for 5 minutes and then walks another 100m and so on, to a maximum of 1200m. Walks are carried out at dawn and in fine weather. If a squirrel is spotted, the distant away from the transect is estimated and recorded, along with behaviour and the tree species it was in. A formula is used to calculate the number of squirrels living in the wood. On the mainland this method is also used to see if greys have moved into a wood and how the red and grey numbers change.

Food leavings

Squirrels eat a wide variety of food, but hazelnuts and fir cones offer the best opportunity of identifying which animal has eaten the nut or cone, as they access the food using their own distinct method. Squirrels open hazelnuts by notching the top of the nut and splitting it in half. Fir cones are stripped of their scales, the seeds extracted and the cores discarded. This method indicates the presence of squirrels.

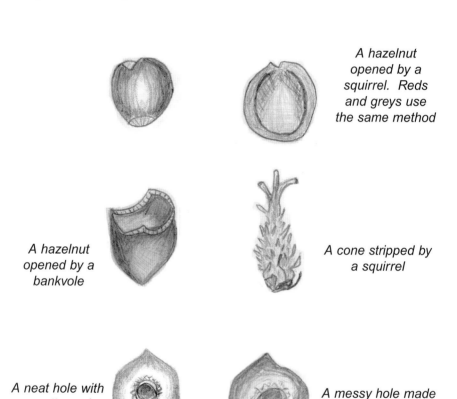

A hazelnut opened by a squirrel. Reds and greys use the same method

A hazelnut opened by a bankvole

A cone stripped by a squirrel

A neat hole with a patterned edge made by a dormouse

A messy hole made by a woodmouse

Hazelnut and pine cone leavings identification chart

Red Squirrel Conservation on the Isle of Wight

Wight Squirrel Project carries out the majority of red squirrel work on the Island. It is a small local charity run by volunteers, headed by the author. Being independent, it is reliant on donations, sponsorship and fund raising. Advice and annual newsletters are free.

Hairtube surveys, woodland monitoring walks, questionnaires, sightings from the general public, post mortems and looking for food leavings are all methods used on the Island, but trapping is unpopular as it is stressful for the squirrels and largely unnecessary. Other conservation efforts are rather more innovative.

Road sign

Unfortunately roads sever many of our woods. Where squirrels are using these woods, a spate of road deaths occur. As many as 8 or 9 may be killed at a single blackspot in one year. Post mortem examinations have shown that, more often than not, squirrels hit the car, rather than the cars run over the squirrel. Efforts to reduce road deaths have had some success.

Road signs have proved futile on the Isle of Wight's busiest roads but help on quieter lanes. Rope bridges are successful, but difficult and expensive to erect and maintain. Third party insurance, sponsorship, somebody to fill the hoppers and landowner permission are necessary. Ropes are only used where very small fragmented populations may be wiped out due to road casualties - and conditions must be favourable.

Ropes literally 'bridge the gap', so trees must partially meet across the road, as squirrels do not like to cross very wide, open expanses. Strong high trees are needed to secure the rope a minimum of 20ft above the road. The positioning of telegraph and electric wires sometimes preclude the use of rope bridges.

Food hoppers are placed either side of the road to encourage the squirrels to climb the trees and cross at this point. However, in the autumn when seeds fall onto road edges, the squirrels may be killed foraging amongst the leaf litter.

These innovations help but cannot replace sympathetic woodland management in the long term effort to save red squirrels.

Squirrel on a food hopper

The Fire Brigade erecting a rope bridge in Ryde, Isle of Wight, June 1996.

This was the first rope bridge in the country and due to it's success, others have followed in the north and in Scotland.

The squirrels had no trouble at all getting used to the idea and deaths have been reduced dramatically.

Using the rope across Calthorpe Road, Ryde Isle of Wight
Photograph courtesy of Janet Dack

This busy road in Wootton on the Isle of Wight, has road signs but they have proved inefffective.

Around 8 squirrels are killed here every year.

Due to the width of the road and the location of telegraph wires it is not feasible to use a conventional rope bridge.

The author is still trying to come up with a viable alternative.

Education is an important part of red squirrel work. Advice is given on request and there are leaflets available. Wight Squirrel Project attends local events to further the red squirrel's cause and raise funds. Talks are given to local groups and clubs. This book and a video also help with education.

Sometimes a squirrel is taken ill in a garden and I am called to capture the animal and take it to the vet. In the majority of cases the squirrel is too ill to survive and the illness untreatable . The stress of being handled is sometimes too much for a healthy animal let alone a sick one. It is sometimes kinder to leave them alone.

The Forestry Commission has provided funds to plant corridors between ancient woodlands which should aid future generations of red squirrels on the Isle of Wight. There are also grants to manage existing woodland and to plant new woods. The Isle of Wight Council has written a 'Red Squirrel Strategy' that advocates the importance of habitat management and corridors.

An aerial shot of a complex of small fragmented woods ,in the north of the Isle of Wight, joined by 'corridors' that the squirrels can travel by. The woods are the areas of dark green.

Small fragmented woods in the centre of the Island are not so easy for squirrels to use.

Raising public awareness of the red squirrels plight is another aspect of red squirrel work and a priority with Wight Squirrel Project. As the red squirrel is an endangered and protected species as well as being appealing, the media are usually keen to run red squirrel stories. The rope bridges in particular seem to appeal to the media and the public.

Understanding how a red squirrel's lives and it's needs are paramount if we are to help it's long term survival. Co-operation from authorities and landowners is also vital of course.

Red squirrel work is a popular subject for the media. This is a French TV crew filming on the Isle of Wight.

How You Can Help

If you have red squirrels in your garden then providing a safe feeding place and a varied diet can help them survive in times of food shortage. Squirrels usually leave gardens in the autumn when their natural food is abundant. Greys will arrive whether you want them to or not!

Report sightings

Where there are red squirrels, with or without greys present, then someone will be monitoring them. Contact your nearest Wildlife Trust for details. If you see a squirrel on the Isle of Wight, contact Wight Squirrel Project. The address is:

Wight Squirrel Project,
PO Box 33,
Ryde,
Isle of Wight,
PO33 1BH

Pick up corpses

These provide useful information about the health of red squirrels in the area. Corpses can provide valuable data without the need to capture live animals. Weight, body measurements, sex and general condition are all recorded as well as cause of death. Contact Wight Squirrel Project if you find a dead squirrel on the Isle of Wight. If you find a dead red elsewhere, ring the local Wildlife Trust.

Look at planning applications

Does a planning application affect red squirrels? Does it break a 'corridor' between woodland or encroach into a wood? Greys do not have the same protection as reds and will not be considered in a planning matter.

If we want to keep our remaining native red squirrels we must all 'do our bit'.

Photograph courtesy of Lyn Hodges

The Law

Red and grey squirrels are mentioned in the Wildlife and Countryside Act 1981 - but for different reasons. Red squirrels and their dreys are partially protected, whilst greys are classed as vermin and it is illegal to release a grey once it is caught.

Red squirrels
It is illegal to:

1) Intentionally kill, injure or take a red squirrel.

2) Possess or control (live or dead animal, part or derivative).

3) Cause damage to, destruction of, obstruction of access to, any structure or place used by a squirrel for shelter or protection.

4) Disturb a red squirrel occupying such a structure or place.

5) Sell, offer for sale, possess or transport for the purpose of sale (live or dead animal, part or derivative).

6) Advertise buying or selling of wild red squirrels.

7) A licence is required to trap red squirrels for scientific purposes.

8) There are certain exceptions. It is legal to nurse or humanely destroy injured red squirrels. There is also provision to cover incidental actions that are an unavoidable result of otherwise lawful activity, eg. if you hit a red squirrel whilst driving. Forestry operations are also exempt as long as reasonable care is taken.

9) Habitat prioritisation is another exception. The Act sets out the roles of English Nature and other organisations delivering Government objectives for wildlife. Red squirrels and woodland are not always seen as a priority.

Grey squirrels

1) It is illegal to bring a grey (even caged) into an area where there are only reds, eg, the Isle of Wight. This offence carries a prison sentence of up to 2 years.

2) Once caught, it is illegal to release a grey squirrel.

3) It is illegal to breed or sell greys.

The Future

The future is impossible to predict accurately. Efforts to captive breed and reintroduce reds have proved difficult. When released into a strange place they panic and bolt. Stress is often followed by illness and death. It could be that red squirrels carry a map of their home range in their head and if released elsewhere they are confused and become stressed.

There are strategies in place to prevent greys taking over the remaining red territory and to retain at least a few populations of red squirrels. Only time will tell if they are effective. Realistically, natural islands such as the Poole harbour islands and the Isle of Wight are the red squirrels' best hope of survival in Great Britain.

It is most important that a fixed link to the Isle of Wight is never built, as it would enable greys to easily reach the Island - as they did in Anglesey.

A female grey squirrel found dead at Freshwater, Isle of Wight in 2001

Large isolated conifer plantations such as Kielder Forest in Northumberland and the pine plantations in Scotland could also provide a haven for the reds - with the grey squirrels controlled.

In Europe, grey squirrels must be prevented from crossing the Alps. Once they become established, as we have seen , it is impossible to eradicate them. Also, once people have accepted the greys, the public is reluctant to see them killed.

Co-operation from landowners, Forestry Authorities, the public and Government departments is paramount if our native red squirrels are to have a future in Great Britain. It seems certain the American grey squirrel is here to stay and is likely to remain the most commonly seen squirrel.

Successful Red Squirrel Spotting

Large forests on the Isle of Wight such as Bouldnor, Firestone and Parkhurst offer good opportunities to see reds. Other attractions such as Robin Hill, Osborne House, Flamingo Park, Fort Victoria, Havenstreet Station, Thorness Holiday Centre and Shanklin Chine also have squirrels.

Brownsea Island in Poole Harbour (summer months only). Contacts: National Trust, Dorset Wildlife Trust.

Formby on Merseyside, belonging to the National Trust, is a very good place to see reds.

Scotland advertises opportunities to see reds in the pine plantations. You can find details on the internet.

The Lake District still has red squirrels. Ring the local Tourist Information Centre or Wildlife Trust for advice.

Tips for spotting reds squirrels in the wild

* Walk slowly and quietly.
* Watch and listen for movement in the trees.
* Listen for the 'chukking' sound of annoyance they make as you approach.
* Take binoculars.
* Leave the dog at home.
* Look for feeding signs such as nibbled fircones or hazelnut shells.
* Look for dreys.
* Dawn and dusk are their most active times.

Red Squirrel Thoughts

Running up and down this rope seems to amuse the humans and the reward is tasty

Hope there isn't a grey stowaway on any of those boats.

It would be worse if there was a bridge or tunnel - we would be doomed

Yipee! More new tree planting. My great, great, great, great, great, great...great grandchildren will be pleased!

With so many species facing extinction, often due to your human activities, please put your efforts into conserving us, your native red squirrels, albeit in only a few locations. The grey squirrel has resisted your efforts to retard its relentless progress into our territory and is here to stay. Where it's feasible, you should make a determined effort to protect us remaining populations of reds. Let's face it - we are well worth it!

Acknowledgements

Over the years there have been many researchers carrying out red squirrel work and giving us the vital information on red squirrel needs. Some of this information is used in this book, which the author gratefully acknowledges.

Other information, on the Isle of Wight, has been gathered by the author over the past 13 years. The majority of this has only been possible due to the efforts and co-operation of volunteers who carry out woodland monitoring walks, people who fill in questionnaires, landowners and the general public who report sightings.

English Nature, The Forestry Commission and the Hants and Wight Wildlife Trust has funded research and surveys carried out by the author.

Thank you to Lyn Hodges, Janet Dack and Dave Dana for their help with some of the photographs.

Thank you to Mary Ralph for allowing me to use her poem.

Thanks to Naomi White, the Adams family and the staff at Flamingo Park, Seaview, Isle of Wight, for their fund raising efforts that went towards producing this book

Helen Butler BSc

Helen has been working voluntarily for red squirrels on the Isle of Wight since 1991 running an independent red squirrel charity. A large part of the work is giving advice, monitoring and raising public awareness of the red squirrel's plight.

This book is aimed at those who are interested in squirrels and would like to gain a better understanding of their life and the problems they face. Grey squirrels are included in the book as their introduction to Britain has had such a devastating effect on our native red squirrels.

Most of the photographs and all the artwork and diagrams were done by the author who is a keen photographer and artist. The facts are easy to find and the pictures clarify the text.

This book will appeal to most age groups and levels of understanding but most of all will gain even more support for our own endangered native woodland mammal - the red squirrel. Here is an opportunity to contrast the 2 species and understand how the American grey squirrel has replaced our native reds.

If you would like to know more about Wight Squirrel Project, please write to: Wight Squirrel Project,
PO Box 33, Ryde,
Isle of Wight, PO33 1BH

ISBN   97809552314-0-7
09552314-0-X

Published by:
RED SQUIRREL ENTERPRISES

Sin, Forgiveness
and Eternal Life

AUTHENTIC
YOUTH BIBLE

COMPILED AND WRITTEN
BY CHIP AND HELEN KENDALL